Contents

CW00545534

The Key

The novel 'Fair's Fair' by Leon Garfield tells the story of a poor orphan boy called Jackson. It is a freezing cold, snowy day, Jackson sits huddled in a doorway and is just about to devour a lovely hot pie when along comes a very large dog. This is what happens next in the story.

He couldn't make up his mind whether it was better to be warm outside or in. He couldn't make up his mind whether it would be better to keep the pie and warm his hands, or to eat it and warm his insides. So there he was, thinking hard, with his face screwed up like a piece of paper, when the black dog came in.

Huge: as big as a donkey, nearly, with eyes like street lamps and jaws like an oven door. Down the street it padded, with a glare to the left, and a savage twitch of its great black nose. Somebody opened a window and threw a bucket of dirty water down; and the black dog snarled with rage. Up it came to the doorstep where Jackson sat and steamed. It glared and growled while the snowflakes fried on its nose.

"Shove off!" wails Jackson, hiding his pie and shaking in his shoes - or rather, in his feet as he had no shoes worth mentioning. "I got no food and I'm only skin and bone myself so I'll taste as sour as leaves!"

"Liar!" says the dog; not in words but with its terrible eyes and rattling teeth.

"I'm froze and hungry!" wails Jackson, wishing he'd eaten the pie.

"And I'm froze and hungry!" says the dog; not in words but with its lean sides and smoking breath.

"All right!" says Jackson, "seeing there's no help for it. Fair's fair. Half for you and half for me." And he breaks the pie and the dog swallows down half with a fearful guzzle and growl.

"Fair's fair," says Jackson; and eats what's left. "Now shove off!"

But the black dog just stands, and bangs at the snow with its tail. Then as big as the night, with its street-lamp eyes it comes straight at Jackson; and licks his face. Not because it loves him, but because Jackson smells as much of pie as he does of drains.

"You're spifflicating me!" howls Jackson, and tries to push the monster off.

He gets his hands round its tree of a neck and then cries out, "Hullo! You got a collar on! You must belong to somebody. Hullo again! You got something under your collar. What you got? Stone the crows! You got a key!"

© **Topical Resources.** May be photocopied for classroom use only

the Key

National Literacy Strategy Year 6 Term 1:

To manipulate narrative perspective by writing in the voice and style of a text.
To plan quickly and effectively the plot, characters and structure of their own narrative writing.

Before reading the extract on the photocopiable page, explain to the children that it is set a long time ago and is about a harmless ragged street urchin called Jackson. The boy has no home, no family, no shoes and is huddled in a doorway just about to eat a hot pie that is his earnings from a day's work, scrubbing a shop floor.

Read the extract aloud to the class, then ask them to read it again to themselves. Ask the children to describe how they imagine Jackson to be. Talk about the evidence from the passage which tells that the story is not set in modern times. Bring out the fact that the dirty water is not poured down a sink or bath but is thrown out of the window into the street, as modern plumbing has not been invented. Talk about the boy's dress and the fact that he has no shoes.
Discuss what happens to children who have no family nowadays and what happened then.
(NOTE This may be a sensitive issue for some children in your class and the teacher should be aware of this.)

Discuss Jackson's personality characteristics - the fact that he is a kind boy and is willing to share with the dog when he is very hungry himself. Ask the children what they think will happen after this episode. Will the key lead him to a house which is occupied? Who might Jackson meet? How do the inhabitants react to the street urchin? What happens to Jackson and the dog? Does the story have a happy or sad ending?

Pick out examples of language from the text which indicate that the story was written a long time ago.

Using the title "The Key", the children should write an imaginary story of what happened to Jackson from the point at which he finds the key, until he discovers the house or building it unlocks and the people Jackson meets there and finally how the story is resolved.

A plan can be made using the writing frame which follows. Emphasise that it is important that the children should try to write in the style of the author Leon Garfield. The children should try to add detail to describe the boy and the dog. The children should attempt to capture the boy's style of speech. It may be helpful to gather together phrases and words that Jackson uses in the passage, for example, "I got no food and I'm only skin and bone...", or "Stone the crows!", or "Fair's fair". These could be incorporated in the children's own writing.

There is also a writing support sheet, for children who have special needs or who struggle to think up ideas for their story.

The Key

Name: _____ **Date:**_____

Here are some words and ideas to help you. Can you add to these?

Setting
Street: crowded, buildings, narrow, dirty, empty, dark, street lamps.

Weather: cold, freezing, snowy, winter, snow flakes.

House: stone, brick, huge / small, garden, overgrown / tidy.

Rooms: large, empty, or full of beautiful furniture, rich / poor.

Language
Words and phrases which make the story seem as if it happened a long time ago.
"I got no food and I'm only skin and bone."
"Stone the crows!"
"Fairs fair!"

Characters

Now put ideas here about the people Jackson meets in your story.

Jackson:
A poor orphan, dirty, torn clothes, lonely, homeless, thin, tired, hungry

The Dog:
'As big as a donkey', black nose, huge jaws.

© **Topical Resources.** May be photocopied for classroom use only.

The Key

Name: _____   **Date:** _____

The story setting:

Characters in the story:

The story begins when Jackson finds a key. What does he do next? What door does the key fit? Does the dog go with him?

What is the building like from the outside and then the inside?

Who does Jackson meet? Are they friendly / unfriendly?

How is the story resolved? Is Jackson taken in or rejected by the people in the house or building?

© **Topical Resources.** May be photocopied for classroom use only.

The Lost Child

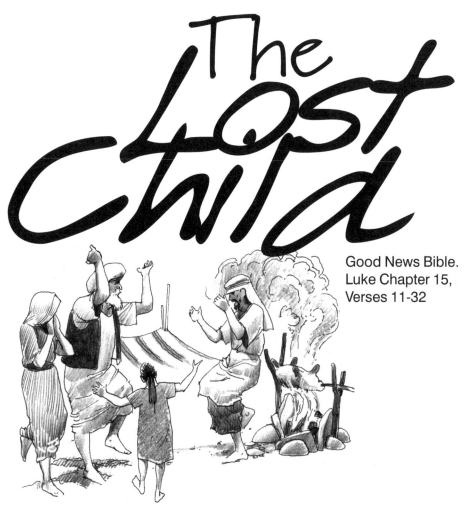

Good News Bible. Luke Chapter 15, Verses 11-32

Jesus went on to say, There was once a man who had two sons. The younger one said to him. "Father, give me my share of the property now." So the man divided his property between his two sons. After a few days the younger son sold his part of the property and left home with the money. He went to a country far away, where he wasted his money in reckless living. He spent everything he had. Then a severe famine spread over that country, and he was left without a thing. So he went to work for one of the citizens of that country, who sent him out to his farm to take care of the pigs. He wished he could fill himself with the bean pods the pigs ate, but no one gave him anything to eat. At last he came to his senses and said, "All my Father's hired workers have more than they can eat, and here I am about to starve! I will get up and go to my Father and say, Father, I

have sinned against God and against you. I am no longer fit to be called your son; treat me as one of your hired workers." So he got up and started back to his Father.

He was still a long way from home when his Father saw him; his heart was filled with pity, and he ran, threw his arms round his son, and kissed him. "Father", the son said, "I have sinned against God and against you. I am no longer fit to be called your son." But the Father called his servants. "Hurry!" he said. "Bring the best robe and put it on him. Put a ring on his finger and shoes on his feet. Then go and get the prize calf and kill it, and let us celebrate with a feast! For this son of mine was dead, but now he is alive; he was lost, but now he has been found." And so the feasting began.

In the meantime the elder son was out in the field. On his

way back, when he came close to the house, he heard the music and dancing. So he called one of the servants and asked him, "What's going on?".
"Your brother has come back home," the servant answered, "and your Father has killed the prize calf because he got him back safe and sound."

The elder brother was so angry that he would not go into the house; so his Father came out and begged him to come in. But he answered his Father, "Look, all these years I have worked for you like a slave, and I have never disobeyed your orders. What have you given me? Not even a goat for me to have a feast with my friends!". "My son," the Father answered, "you are always here with me, and everything I have is yours. But we had to celebrate and be happy, because your brother was dead, but now he is alive; he was lost, but now he has been found."

© **Topical Resources.** May be photocopied for classroom use only.

National Literacy Strategy Year 6 Term 1:

To manipulate narrative perspective by producing a modern re-telling.
To plan quickly and effectively the plot, characters and structure of their own narrative writing.

Read the passage aloud to the children at least twice. Ask the children about the events in the story to ensure they have understood the sequence of the narrative. Together, make a plan of the narrative events in chronological order on the board.

Talk about the children's own ideas for making a modern version of the story. For example, instead of a famine, it might be that the present crisis in farming has affected the farmer. Perhaps reckless living might be visiting too many night clubs or spending money on staying in expensive hotels.

It would be a useful activity at this stage to put the children into groups of four or five and to ask them together to make their own modern version of the story. This could be done as a role-play and might be shared with other children in the class. Role-play can be a useful tool for generating ideas prior to writing.

The children should then make their plan of a modern re-telling using the writing frame. There is also a writing support sheet for those children who struggle to record their ideas.

When the children have planned carefully, the story can then be written under the title "The Lost Child" or an alternative of their own.

The Lost Child

Name: _____ **Date:** _____

Tom was fed up! He hated living on the farm. It was so boring.

_____
_____
_____

He decided to ask his dad for the money he had been saving for Tom. Then, he could go to Spain for the Summer.

_____
_____
_____
_____

Tom got on a plane. After two hours he arrived in Spain. He was going to have fun!

_____
_____
_____
_____

Soon he found he had no money left. All his new friends had gone. He would have to find a job.

_____
_____
_____
_____

"What a fool I have been!" thought Tom. "I think I'll go home."

_____
_____
_____
_____

When he got there, his Dad was so pleased to see him. "I'm so glad you have come home," Dad said, putting his arm around Tom. "Let's have a party!" Tom's brother did not look very happy.

_____
_____
_____
_____

 © **Topical Resources.** May be photocopied for classroom use only.

The Lost Child

Writing Frame

Name: _____   **Date:** _____

The story setting:

Characters in the story:

The story begins when the child asks for the money he should inherit. Where does he/she go?

What happens when he/she gets there? Who does he/she meet? What happens?

What goes wrong and how does he/she lose his/her money? How does he/she survive?

What happens when he/she returns home? How does the story end?

© Topical Resources. May be photocopied for classroom use only.

11

Hagrid's Story

From 'Harry Potter and the Philosopher's Stone' by J. K. Rowling

In this excerpt, Harry Potter, who has lived with his unkind Aunt and Uncle, the Dursleys since he was orphaned as a baby, is about to learn about his parents and his past. The Giant Hagrid has come from Hogwarts School of Witchcraft and Wizardry to bring Harry back there to study.

The giant took a gulp of tea and wiped his mouth with the back of his hand.

'Call me Hagrid,' he said, 'everyone does. An' like I told yeh, I'm Keeper of Keys at Hogwarts - yeh'll know all about Hogwarts, o' course.'

'Er - no,' said Harry.

Hagrid looked shocked.

'Sorry,' Harry said quickly.

'Sorry?' barked Hagrid, turning to stare at the Dursleys, who shrank back into the shadows. 'It's them as should be sorry! I knew yeh weren't gettin' yer letters but I never thought yeh wouldn't even know abou' Hogwarts, fer cryin' out loud! Did yeh never wonder where yer parents learnt it all?'

'All what?' asked Harry.

'ALL WHAT?' Hagrid thundered. 'Now wait jus' one second!'

He had leapt to his feet. In his anger he seemed to fill the whole hut. The Dursleys were cowering against the wall.

'Do you mean ter tell me,' he growled at the Dursleys, 'that this boy - this boy! - knows nothin' abou' - about ANYTHING?'

Harry thought this was going a bit far. He had been to school, after all, and his marks weren't bad.

'I know some things,' he said. 'I can, you know, do maths and stuff.'

But Hagrid simply waved his hand and said, 'About our world, I mean. Your world. My world. Yer parents' world.'

'What world?'

Hagrid looked as if he was about to explode.

'DURSLEY,' he boomed.

Uncle Vernon, who had gone very pale, whispered something that sounded like 'Mimblewimble'. Hagrid stared wildly at Harry.

'But yeh must know about yer mum and dad,' he said. 'I mean, they're famous. You're famous.'

'What? My - my mum and dad weren't famous, were they?'

'Yeh don' know ... yeh don' know ...' Hagrid ran his fingers through his hair, fixing Harry with a bewildered stare.

'Yeh don' know what yeh are?' he said finally.

Uncle Vernon suddenly found his voice.

'Stop!' he commanded. 'Stop right there sir! I forbid you to tell the boy anything!'

A braver man than Vernon Dursley would have quailed under the furious look Hag now gave him; when Hagrid spoke, his every syllable trembled with rage.

'You never told him? Never told him wha was in the letter Dumbledore left fer him' was there! I saw Dumbledore leave it, Dursley! An' you've kept it from him all these years?'

'Kept what from me?' said Harry eagerly.

'STOP! I FORBID YOU!' yelled Uncle Vernon in panic. Aunt Petunia gave a ga of horror.

'Ah, go boil yer heads, both of yeh,' said Hagrid. 'Harry - yer a wizard.'

© **Topical Resources.** May be photocopied for classroom use only.

Hagrid's Story

National Literacy Strategy Year 6 Term 1:

To manipulate narrative perspective by writing a story with two different narrators.

Read the passage aloud to the children. Some of the class may have read Harry Potter and the Philosopher's Stone. Explain that Harry's existence, up to that point, had been a very unhappy time. He was orphaned as a baby and had been left on the doorstep of his Aunt and Uncle, the Dursleys. The Dursleys disliked Harry, favouring their own son Dudley, who was thoroughly spoilt. Whilst Harry's bedroom was a cupboard, Dudley was showered with gifts and presents. Harry knew nothing of his parents. The Dursleys hid from Harry all details of his background.

Ask the children to write the story from the point at which the passage ends. How do they think Harry reacted to the revelation that he is a wizard? What questions might he ask Hagrid? They should go on to imagine that Hagrid tells Harry about his parents who were wizards. He might relate something wonderful or exciting that Harry's parents achieved as wizards. The story should end with Harry's reaction to the story he has just been told. The children should plan their story using the writing frame provided.

When the story is planned, the children can write the story in full. There is a writing support sheet for those members of the group who lack ideas or who have special needs. This is a partly completed writing frame, as some children may find this a difficult activity.

It is important that the children try to incorporate Hagrid's story as a story within a story. Their story should begin in the third person, narrating the reaction of Harry to Hagrid's news. As they move on to the part of their story where Hagrid relates to Harry, his parents' story, the children should write as though they are Hagrid himself. This will be difficult for some children to achieve. Prior to the children beginning to write, it would be valuable for the teacher to model part of the writing activity on the board. This would aid the children's understanding of which tense and person to use when writing.

Name: _____ **Date:** _____

Harry could not believe his ears. "My parents were wizards! Wow!" he thought to himself in real amazement. "Did they look like me or were they like wizards in story books?" he asked Hagrid with excitement. _____

_____
_____
_____

"Now Harry, let me tell you all about them and some of the wonderful things they did," Hagrid replied.

The Story of Mr and Mrs Potter

"I remember oh so well the day they did the most amazing thing!....." _____

_____
_____
_____
_____
_____
_____
_____
_____
_____
_____
_____
_____

Harry was shocked, filled with pride, but sad too. Oh how he wished he had met his parents! He wanted them to know _____

_____
_____
_____
_____
_____
_____
_____

Harry thought about his new school, Hogwarts, a School for Wizards. _____

_____
_____
_____
_____
_____
_____

© **Topical Resources.** May be photocopied for classroom use only.

Hagrid's Story

Writing Frame

Name: _____ **Date:** _____

The story setting:

Characters in the story:

As the story begins what is Harry's reaction to Hagrid's news that his parents were wizards?

Story within a story - **Hagrid's Story**. What are some of the wonderful things Hagrid remembers Harry's parents doing?

Back to Harry. What is his reaction to the story? What does he feel about being a wizard and going to Hogwarts School?

© **Topical Resources.** May be photocopied for classroom use only.

15

Peter and the Wolf
A Traditional Tale

There was once a boy called Peter, who lived in a small house on the edge of a large forest. Peter lived with his grandfather, a kind and wise old man. Peter had three best friends, a duck, a cat and a bird. The duck lived in a duck pond which was close by Peter's garden. Peter would often fish in the pond and the duck would keep him company. The cat was beautiful, black and white and loved to chase string or marbles when Peter was playing. Peter loved the cat dearly. His friend the bird would chirp each morning, outside Peter's bedroom window and he would go and find her.

Peter's Grandfather worried about Peter straying too far away. He knew that in the forest were wolves and he worried that Peter might come to harm. "Do not go near the forest Peter!" he warned. "You know there are wolves there!"

Unfortunately even though Peter loved each of his friends dearly, the three friends did not like each other. One day as Peter was fishing in the pond, the bird began to tease the duck. It flew around the duck's head and shouted, "What a stupid duck you are! You can't fly like me. You can only swim on a pond. What a useless creature you are!" The cat who was sitting next to Peter almost caught the bird one day. It flew up to the high branches of a tree out of reach of the cat.

However a wolf had crept out of the forest and spotted the duck swimming on the pond and gobbled him up at once. Peter afraid, ran quickly back to his garden and bolted the gate. The wolf sat there looking up at the cat and the bird, licking his lips and feeling very hungry indeed.

Peter was desperate to help his friends. "What can I do?" he thought to himself anxiously. Then he had an idea. He brought a rope from the shed and climbed up a tree next to the garden wall. He whispered to the bird, "Fly down and circle the wolf's nose." At first the little bird was scared but she decided to do as Peter asked, as he was her friend. Soon she teased the wolf and how she enjoyed it! The angry wolf, snapped and growled at the little bird. Very quickly and quietly, Peter lowered a loop of rope around the wolf's tail. He pulled the rope tight and the wolf was caught!

As it happened, there were some hunters passing by. They had been hunting for wolves in the forest and when they saw the wolf caught by its tail, they rushed to help Peter. They tied the wolf up and took him to the Zoo and Peter lived happily ever after!

© Topical Resources. May be photocopied for classroom use only.

Peter and the Wolf

National Literacy Strategy Year 6 Term 1:

To summarise a passage, chapter or text, in a specified number of words.

Read aloud the story of Peter and the Wolf on the photocopiable page (if possible listen to the music by Prokofiev). It would be helpful for the children to read the story again, so that they become familiar with the sequence of events. Ask the children to briefly map out the events in rough.

The children should then summarise the story in no more than 150 words.
Important points to emphasise to the children when they are writing summaries are as follows:
1. Write your summary in the 3rd person, e.g. In the story Peter had three friends.
2. Write it, as though it happened in the past, e.g. The story told how Peter's Grandfather worried about the boy.
3. Leave out unimportant details. Only pick out the vital parts of the story.
4. Do not copy from the story. It will be much easier to write a summary, in your own words, from the map of events you make.

It would be useful to have the above instructions displayed in the classroom, as a guide for the children while they work.

A useful follow up activity would be to read the summaries aloud and to discuss together whether they are successful. Have they included all the important parts of the story? Are there any details that have been included which could have been omitted? When doing this kind of critical activity, it is important to emphasise that criticism should be constructive. The children should remember to be respectful towards each individual's work when they are criticising. They should always begin by saying something positive about the work done. If not feelings can be hurt!

For children who have special needs or who struggle with the activity, there is a support sheet. This simple writing frame is partly completed.

Peter and the Wolf

Name: _____ **Date:** _____

Peter was _____

_____

_____

Peter's friends were _____

_____

They liked to _____

_____

_____

Peter's Grandfather warned _____

_____

The friends did not listen _____

_____

_____

One day the bird _____

_____

Along came _____

_____

Peter wanted to help his friends so _____

_____

_____

Then along came _____

_____

_____

  © **Topical Resources.** May be photocopied for classroom use only.

Peter and the Wolf

Name: _____ **Date:** _____

Map out the main events in the story of Peter and the Wolf.

The main events in paragraph 1 are:

The main events in paragraph 2 are:

The main events in paragraph 3 are:

The main events in paragraph 4 are:

The main events in paragraph 5 are:

The main events in paragraph 6 are:

© **Topical Resources.** May be photocopied for classroom use only.

19

The Three Little Pigs

A Traditional Tale

Once upon a time there were three little pigs. As they were quite grown up, their Mother sent them away to look for a new home. She warned them about the big bad wolf who enjoyed eating pigs for his supper!

The pigs set out to find a new home. The first pig met a man with some straw. Politely he asked for some to make a house. The man gave him the straw and he built his house and was pleased with it. "The big bad wolf cannot get me here," he thought.

The second pig met a man with some sticks. The man gave him some of them to make a house. The second pig was pleased with the house and was sure the big bad wolf would not be able to get him once he was inside.

The third pig met a man who gave him bricks to build his house from. He too was pleased with his house and said, "The big bad wolf cannot get me now!"

The big bad wolf saw the house of straw and decided he could easily get the little pig. "Little pig, let me come in!" the wolf begged. "No no, by the hair on my chinny, chin chin!" replied the pig. "Then I'll huff and I'll puff and I'll blow your house down!" snarled the wolf angrily. He huffed and puffed and sure enough, down came the house of straw and the little pig was eaten up!

The wolf, then went to the house made of sticks, asking to be let in. The pig refused and the wolf huffed and puffed and blew the house down. In an instant the second little pig was eaten by the big bad wolf.

The wolf then went to the house made of bricks and again asked to be let in. He huffed and puffed. He got more and more cross, as the house of bricks stood firm. The wolf could not blow it down! He then climbed onto the roof of the house made of bricks. Inside the little pig was making some hot broth. All of a sudden down fell the wolf into the hot broth and met his end! The little pig had no more worries and lived in the housee of bricks happily every after!

© **Topical Resources.** May be photocopied for classroom use only.

National Literacy Strategy Year 6 Term1:

To prepare a short section of story as a script, e.g. using stage directions / location / setting.

Read the story aloud to the children. Ask them to choose a part of the story to make into a play script. Model a section of play script on the board. Emphasise the importance of layout and writing in the present tense. Explain that stage directions should be written in brackets. The scene should be preceded by a list of Characters who appear. Following this will be details of location/setting.

It would be useful if groups of children were to cover different parts of the story. Each small scene, could then be pieced together to form a complete script of the story 'The Three Little Pigs.' These could then be acted out.

A useful follow up would be to evaluate the success of their scripts. If the children are to criticise or discuss each other's work, then it is important to emphasise that the criticism should contain positive comments as well as negative comments. It is important that criticism is constructive.

The children may well need several attempts to come up with a script that they are satisfied with. It is important here that opportunity is made for drafting. Access to a Word Processing programme would be helpful.

For children who struggle with this activity or who have special needs, there is a writing support sheet.

Name: _____ **Date:** _____

The Three Little Pigs Leave Home

Characters

Mother Pig

Sam   The first pig who built his house of straw

Tim   The second pig who built

Ben   The third pig

(The story is set in Mother Pig's house. She has gathered the three little pigs together to talk to them.)

Mother	Come here little pigs. I have something I must tell you.
Pigs	(together) All right Mother!
Mother	(brings the little pigs close to her) Now Sam, Tim and Ben, you are all quite grown up _____ _____
Sam	Mother I will miss you!
Tim	_____
Ben	_____
Mother	I will miss you too! You can come and
Sam	I must go and pack!
Tim	_____
Ben	_____
	(The three little pigs go off. Then they return to say goodbye to their Mother.)
Sam	(sadly)
Tim	(mopping his tears)
Ben	_____
Mother	_____
	(The three little pigs walk off

© **Topical Resources.** May be photocopied for classroom use only.

Name: _____ **Date:** _____

The Three Little Pigs Leave Home

Characters

Setting

© **Topical Resources.** May be photocopied for classroom use only.

Poems with Active Verbs and Personification

Autumn

I shorten the days,
Turn leaves from green to burnished gold,
Make fruit, ripe, plump and juicy.
I dash around the garden,
Shaking leaves from brown branches.
I light bonfires,
Whose smoke curls up to the dull grey sky.
I chase hedgehogs into piles of leaves to sleep,
For the Winter soon creeps up behind me!
I am Autumn.

Happiness

I make people giggle!
I tell them jokes, pull funny faces,
And make them smile.
I give them birthdays, Christmas,
Easter eggs.
I give but never take away.
I give a bunch of flowers to
The lovely old lady.
A wave, a handshake, a gentle
touch, a hug I give, to all I meet.
I am happiness.

Anger

I smack, hit and kick,
I throw my friend's ball on the roof.
I tear pages out of my homework when
the sums are wrong.
I have a face as red as a fire engine
and hot as a bonfire.
I shout words that I later wish
I hadn't said.
My friend is hate,
for I am ANGER!

24

© **Topical Resources.** May be photocopied for classroom use only.

Poems with Active Verbs and Personification

National Literacy Strategy Year 6 Term1:

To write own poems experimenting with active verbs and personification; produce revised poems for reading aloud.

Read aloud the poems on the photocopiable page, at least twice. Explain that the subject of each poem is something abstract - a feeling or a season. Ask the children how each of the feelings/seasons have been described. Explain that the poets have written them, as though they are actually people. This is called personification. Go through each poem and ask the children to explain what aspects or features are being described. Explain to the children the meaning of active verbs. Pick examples of these out from the poems e.g.: I shorten, I dash around, I light etc.

As a class, choose a title, e.g. Sadness, Spring, Darkness and compose a poem written in the first person just as those on the photocopiable page are written in the first person. Write it up line by line on the board. Together re-work each line adding adjectives, or more descriptive words until you have a final draft class poem.

Using this experience, as a model for their own writing, children should then individually choose their own title and compose their own personal poem in the same way. It should be re-worked until the children feel satisfied with their revised version. These should then be read aloud and put together in a class anthology.

For children who find this activity difficult, or children who have special needs, there is a writing support sheet.

Poems with Active Verbs and Personification

Name: _____ **Date:** _____

Poems with active verbs and personification

Here are some opening lines to help you start writing. Can you add more of your own? Don't forget to imagine that summer or sadness is a person. Start with the title that appeals to you most.

Summer
I paint the sky blue,
I dig in the sand building tall castles,
I cover the garden in flowers blue, yellow and purple.

Sadness
I make people cry,
I cut fingers and skin knees,
I make flowers wither,
I break your favourite toy.

Fear
I creep about in the dark and scare you!
I am a great hairy spider on the bedroom wall,
I am noises that make you jump out of your skin!

Darkness
I wrap up the sky in a great black blanket,
My friends are the moon and the stars,
I close children's eyes making them sleep.

 © Topical Resources. May be photocopied for classroom use only.

School Uniform
yes or no?

Here we have two very different ways of looking at school uniform. Is there a middle road in all of this? What do you think?

School Uniform, Say "NO!"

School Uniform! Those two words bring a spine chilling feeling of sheer dread to thousands of young people! The drab colours - grey, green or navy blue or even black evoke that feeling of Monday morning, when you wake up and realise Saturday is five whole days away! Why on earth should we have to be dressed all the same like identical cans of beans on a factory assembly line? Surely, our own personality, our own identity is hidden, beneath dull school skirts, trousers and jumpers!

If pupils were allowed to wear their own choice of clothes, then surely they would feel more at ease and therefore more inclined to give their best in all aspects of school life. Work and behaviour standards would improve dramatically and school would be a much more pleasant place for both teachers and pupils.

Parents too would be happier. They would save time and money on visits to expensive School Uniform Shops, in August when funds are generally low after the summer holidays.

Stay Smart Stay in Uniform!

It is vital that we keep school uniform and maintain a tradition that has been in existence for years. It is traditions like these which make the English Education system the envy of the world! School uniform brings discipline, encourages good behaviour and sets standards which will ensure pupils give of their best. The garments are simple, easily replaced and kept clean.

They prevent 'Mr Rich's' son from becoming the hero just because he has the right designer label. School Uniform is a way of giving everyone the same chance, the same opportunity, of making everyone equal. Whatever happens, school uniform must stay!

© **Topical Resources.** May be photocopied for classroom use only.

27

School Uniform  yes or no?

National Literacy Strategy Year 6 Term 2:

To write commentaries or summaries crediting views expressed by using expressions such as "The writer says that...."

Read the articles aloud to the children ensuring that they read them again for themselves. These articles could introduce a class discussion on the topic. Then ask the children to list the main arguments for and against uniform. It may be useful to list the important points on the board, depending on how much experience the children have of summary activities. Encourage the children to express their ideas in their own words and not just to copy from the text.

The children should then use the ideas to make a summary. The summary of the ideas in the articles should be put into two separate paragraphs, one giving the arguments for and the other against. Each paragraph should begin with the words:
"The writer says that...." Again, emphasis should be placed on ensuring that this is in the children's own words and that sections are not just copied from the passage. For those children who struggle with this activity or who have little previous experience of summarising, there is a writing support sheet. It would be useful to display these following instructions for the children:

1   Write your summary in the 3rd person.
2   Begin each paragraph with "The writer says that...."
3   Leave out unimportant details.
4   Try to write in your own words and avoid copying from the articles.

A further useful activity might be to ask each child to write a commentary on the articles, expressing their own opinion on the matter. This could be entitled 'My views on School Uniform'. Again, this would be best done following up a whole class discussion on the topic.

School Uniform *yes or no?*

Name: _____   **Date:** _____

In the first article, the writer argues that school uniform, is not a good idea.
The writer thinks that it is not good because

_____

_____

_____

He also thinks that

_____

If pupils were to wear their own clothes then

_____

_____

Also life is made easier for parents because

_____

_____

In the second article, the writer argues that uniform is a good idea, because

_____

_____

He thinks that uniform makes people

_____

_____

The uniform is easily

_____

_____

It also stops wealthy children

_____

_____

© **Topical Resources.** May be photocopied for classroom use only.

The Great Revolt!

From 'Animal Farm' by George Orwell

Major the pig spoke and the farm animals listened. 'Now, comrades, what is the nature of this life of ours? Let us face it: our lives are miserable, laborious, and short. We are born, we are given just so much food as will keep the breath in our bodies, and those of us who are capable of it are forced to work to the last atom of our strength; and the very instant that our usefulness has come to an end we are slaughtered with hideous cruelty. No animal in England knows the meaning of happiness or leisure after he is a year old. No animal in England is free. The life of an animal is misery and slavery: that is the plain truth.'

'But is this simply part of the order of nature? Is it because this land of ours is so poor that it cannot afford a decent life to those who dwell upon it? No, comrades, a thousand times no! The soil of England is fertile, its climate is good, it is capable of affording food in abundance to an enormously greater number of animals than now inhabit it. This single farm of ours would support a dozen horses, twenty cows, hundreds of sheep - and all of them living in a comfort and a dignity that are now almost beyond our imagining. Why then do we continue in this miserable condition? Because nearly the whole of the produce of our labour is stolen from us by human beings. There, comrades, is the answer to all our problems. It is summed up in a single word - Man. Man is the only real enemy we have. Remove Man from the scene, and the root cause of hunger and overwork is abolished for ever.'

'Man is the only creature that consumes without producing. He does not give milk, he does not lay eggs, he is too weak to pull the plough, he cannot run fast enough to catch rabbits. Yet he is lord of all the animals.

He sets them to work, he gives back to them the bare minimum that will prevent them from starving, and the rest he keeps for himself. Our labour tills the soil, our dung fertilises it, and yet there is not one of us that owns more than his bare skin. You cows that I see before me, how many thousands of gallons of milk have you given during this last year? And what has happened to that milk which should have been breeding up sturdy calves? Every drop of it has gone down the throats of our enemies. And you hens, how many eggs have you laid this last year, and how many of those eggs ever hatched into chickens? The rest have all gone to market to bring in money for Jones and his men. And you, Clover, where are those four foals you bore, who should have been the support and pleasure of your old age? Each was sold at a year old - you will never see one of them again. In return for your four confinements and all your labour in the field, what have you ever had except your bare rations and a stall?'

'Is it not crystal clear, then, comrades, that all the evils of this life of ours spring from the tyranny of human beings? Only get rid of Man, and the produce of our labour would be our own. Almost overnight we could become rich and free.'

 © **Topical Resources**. May be photocopied for classroom use only.

The Great Revolt!

National Literacy Strategy Year 6 Term 2:

To use different genres to write additional episodes, alternative endings, using appropriate conventions, language.

Read the section from 'Animal Farm' aloud. The children should then read the passage again to themselves. Ask the children what Major the pig was saying in his speech? What do you think Major wants the animals to do? What do you think might happen next?

The children should then talk about the idea of a rebellion, what this means and whether they think the farm animals may be successful or not. Talk about the problems the animals may encounter and the aspects that they might enjoy after the rebellion, or the problems they might face.

The children should go on to plan, the story with the title 'The Great Revolt!' It could begin from the start of the rebellion and describe what took place, and finally whether the rebellion was successful or a failure. The children need to think about the characters involved. Might Major the pig be a leader or does another individual or group of animals take the lead?

When the children have planned their story, using the writing frame which follows, they can then begin to write the story in full. There is also a writing support sheet which can aid those children with special needs, or those who struggle to think of ideas for their story.

The Great Revolt!

Name: _____ **Date:** _____

Here are some words and ideas to help you. Can you add to these?

Setting
farm, animals, pigs - Major, Clover,
horse, foal, goats, sheep, farmer, wife,
farmhouse, fields, barn, countryside.

Characters
Major the Pig - leader
Pigs - wise clever speakers
Sly Piglets - squeal squeak
Clover - a horse
Horses - strong brave
Sheep - flock helpers
Goats - stubborn
Farmer - Mr Jones - kind/cruel??

The Revolt
exciting
noisy
fighting
plan together
win/lose
hurt
cuts/bruises
imprison

 © **Topical Resources.** May be photocopied for classroom use only.

The Great Revolt!

Writing Frame

Name: _____ Date: _____

The story setting:

Characters in the story:

The story begins where the animals plan the rebellion. What are their plans?

How do they put their plans into action?

What is the result of the rebellion? Are they happy? What happens to the farmer?

How is the story resolved? Does the farmer return or do the animals remain in charge?

© Topical Resources. May be photocopied for classroom use only.

Grandma's Story

"I'm not going back. I'm not, Grandma, I'm not going back!" Sally wailed as she ran into her Grandma's house.

"Sally, love, calm down, everything's going to be all right," her Grandma whispered, pulling Sally into her arms. "Shh, it will be okay sweetheart, really, it will be just fine."

Sally was nine years old and had just started a new school. She was a hard-working serious child who wanted to do well at school, but who also needed a best friend to share her worries and fears.

Sally had left her best friend at Lowood School, on the other side of the city. Moving house had meant Sally had to change school to Selby Grove Primary, a school on the smart new estate the family had come to live on.

"I hate it Grandma, I'm never going back! Nobody wants to be my friend. Everyone hates me! Oh how I wish I was still at Lowood with Jenny and the others," Sally sobbed. "Oh, now, now, Sally, its only your first day. Give it a chance!" Grandma said comfortingly. "Tell me what happened."

"In the morning, when I arrived and Mum left me on the playground, this horrible boy laughed at me and told me I'd come to the wrong school. I tried to explain that my new school uniform hadn't arrived, so that was why I was wearing the Lowood one, but he wouldn't listen. He just kept laughing and calling me names. Then, when I was in class Miss Burton, my new teacher, asked if anyone would like to look after me at playtime but no-one put their hand up, well not at first, but then this girl called Emma said she would. I know she didn't want to really."

"Oh Sally, I know just what you're feeling. You know, the same thing happened to me. Its really hard at first, but you've got to keep trying. You can't give up after your first day you know," Grandma pleaded.

"Dinner time was awful Gran. This girl Emma let me sit with her for dinner but I knew she really wanted to sit next to her best friend Kate. I kept thinking about Jenny and all my friends at Lowood and I just felt more and more miserable. Then the horrible boy who teased me in the playground came and asked me again if I had come to the wrong school because I was wearing the wrong uniform. All his friends laughed. Emma told him to go away and leave me alone. I hate it I really do!"

"Oh, Sally love, tomorrow it will be better, honestly it will. Just the same happened to me when I was your age. Let me tell you all about it........"

34

© **Topical Resources.** May be photocopied for classroom use only.

Grandma's Story

National Literacy Strategy Year 6 Term 2:

To write own story using e.g. flashbacks or a story within a story to convey the passing of time.

Read the passage aloud to the class. Talk about what has happened to Sally? Can the children relate similar experiences of their own? Has there been a time when they joined a new group where they knew no-one? Can they understand how Sally is feeling? Then ask them how they think the story continues. What happened to Grandma? Why had she moved? Was she perhaps evacuated during the war or did her father move jobs to a different area? What problems did she face? How did the new children in her new class respond to her? Did Grandma's story have a happy ending?

Go on to talk about how Grandma's story affects Sally. Does Sally follow Grandma's advice? Does she return to school and is she happier or does she still feel like an outsider?

The children should then make a plan of their story which begins where the photocopiable excerpt leaves off. The children should tell Grandma's story in the first person, writing as though they are Grandma. Their story should end by returning to Sally's problem, and the effect Grandma's story has on her grand-daughter's situation. The story should end where Sally returns to school, explaining how she gets on when she has her next day at her new school.

There is a writing frame to aid the children's planning and a writing support sheet for those members of the group who lack ideas or who have special needs.

Grandma's Story

Name: _____ **Date:** _____

I remember when I was a little girl of just eight years of age. Our family moved from the city to the countryside. How different the place and the people were!

_____

_____

_____

_____

The day I started at the village school, I felt so nervous.

_____

_____

_____

_____

Then, a little girl, Susan, came over to talk to me. She lived in the next row of cottages.

_____

_____

_____

_____

I went to play at Susan's house. _____

_____

_____

_____

She became my best friend.
Sally listened to Granny's story. She really hadn't tried very hard that day at school to make new friends. Tomorrow would be different.
So the next day _____

_____

_____

_____

 © **Topical Resources.** May be photocopied for classroom use only.

Grandma's Story

Name: _____ **Date:** _____

The story setting:

Characters in the story:

The story begins. Why did Grandma move schools? What happened to her when she started school?

What made things change for Grandma?

What happens to Sally when she goes back the next day?

How is the story resolved? Does Grandma's story affect Sally?

Remember you are going to write your story in the first person as though you <u>are</u> Grandma. When you come to the part of the story where Sally returns to school, write that part of your story in the third person e.g.. Sally went back to school.... etc

© **Topical Resources.** May be photocopied for classroom use only.

Black Jack

From Black Jack by Leon Garfield

Black Jack by Leon Garfield, begins with a public hanging of the seven foot tall ruffian Black Jack. A young boy Bartholomew Dorking, is persuaded to help take the body of the giant back to the house of a woman Mrs Gorgandy. Bartholomew believes her to be a grieving relative. She is however, engaged in the business of selling bodies to doctors for research. Young Dorking is left, as day is fading to guard the body until Mrs Gorgandy returns. This is how the story continues.......

Now, little by little, the moon climbed, out of the invisible chimney pots, turning the window to dull silver, so that it hung on the dark wall like an old tarnished mirror, capable of nothing but spite.

With a sigh of relief Dorking heard a clock strike nine. His vigil was almost done. He stood up and began to walk softly about the room - to ease the cramp in his legs and ward off the night's chill.

The silver moonlight, very bright now, seemed to lend the dingy room an odd beauty - as if it was intricately fashioned out of shining grey lead. Even the coffin and the still ruffian within it seemed carved and moulded by a master hand.

How finely done was the tangled hair - the knotted brow - the powerful, thick nose.... how life-like were the deep grey lips. How - how miraculously shone the moon in the profound eyes - In the eyes? In the eyes? Sure to God those eyes had been shut before?

Those eyes! They were open wide! They were moving! They were staring at him!

Bartholomew Dorking, sent from Shoreham to London to be spared the perils of the sea, stood almost dead of terror.

'Alive!' he moaned. 'He's alive!'

More dreadful than violent death itself was this reviving from it.

A deep, rattling sigh filled the room. Black Jack's chest heaved - and his box crackled ominously. His moon-filled eyes rolled fiercely at Bartholomew.

"Alive!' groaned the boy. 'He's alive!'

© **Topical Resources.** May be photocopied for classroom use only.

Black Jack

National Literacy Strategy Year 6 Term 2:

To study in depth one genre and to produce an extended piece of similar writing, e.g. for inclusion in a class anthology; to plan, revise, redraft this and bring to presentation standard, e.g. layout, paragraphing, accuracy of punctuation and spelling, handwriting/printing.

The novel 'Black Jack' by Leon Garfield, could be studied in depth as an example of historical genre. The section on the photocopiable page comes at a very early stage of the book and the pupil writing activity suggested here could be carried out as the passage is reached. The photocopiable passage is an atmospheric piece of writing which builds up a real feeling of suspense in the reader. Read the section of story aloud to the children. Ask the children what it is about the content and style of the passage, that makes them realise it is not modern? Bring out the idea of a hanging being seen as a public event two hundred years ago. Talk about the sort of crimes which resulted in hanging. Talk about the idea of illegally selling the dead bodies for medical research. Go on to talk about the language of the passage and the ways in which this indicates the passage is not 20th century. It would be useful to gather together words and phrases, which make the passage seem exciting and which add to the sense that it is set in the past.

The children could go on to predict what they think might happen next in the story. Does 'Black Jack' get out of the coffin? Might he take Bartholomew prisoner? Does he perhaps befriend Bartholomew?

The children should then go on to plan and write the chapter or section which follows the photocopiable passage. The children should go through the process of planning using the story writing frame, then writing the story in full. There is a writing support sheet for those children who struggle to find ideas or who have special needs. When the story is written in first draft form they will then need to re-draft looking carefully at paragraphs, punctuation and spelling. The final product could either be word processed on the computer or hand written. The finished products could be put into the child's writing folder or put together into a class anthology of writing.

Black Jack

Name: _____ **Date:** _____

Here are some words and ideas to help you. Can you add these?

Setting
Mrs Gorgandy's House:
dark, dirty, old, cobwebs,
candle-lit, chilly, dingy
room, moonlight

**The place that Black
Jack and Bartholomew
go to:**
town/country, streets,
fields, cottage, hide-away.

Characters
Bartholomew Dorking:
young boy, kind, helpful,
scared/terrified, looks
around carefully, prisoner,
friendly.

Black Jack:
thief, giant, tangled hair,
strong,
ugly/kind/cruel/fierce?

 © **Topical Resources.** May be photocopied for classroom use only.

Black Jack

Name: _____ **Date:** _____

The story setting:

Characters in the story:

The opening of the story when Bartholomew realises Black Jack is alive. What happens?

What happens next? Is Bartholomew taken prisoner by Black Jack? Where do they go?

How is the story resolved? Do they become friends? Does Bartholomew escape? Is Black Jack caught?

© **Topical Resources.** May be photocopied for classroom use only.

THE CIRCUS

The story is set in Victorian Times. The Gradgrind children have been brought up very strictly. Their father believes they should spend their time learning facts. He believes there is no time to waste enjoying life or having fun. One day the children decide to make a secret visit to the circus. Unfortunately, their father catches them watching the circus acts. This is how the story continues...

Dumb with amazement, Mr Gradgrind crossed to the spot where his family was thus disgraced, laid his hand upon each erring child, and said :

"Louisa! Thomas!"

Both rose, red and disconcerted. But, Louisa looked at her father with more boldness than Thomas did. Indeed, Thomas did not look at him, but gave himself up to be taken home like a machine.

"In the name of wonder, idleness, and folly!" said Mr Gradgrind, leading each away by a hand; "what do you do here ?"

"Wanted to see what it was like," returned Louisa shortly.

" What it was like?"

"Yes, father."........

"Thomas, though I have the fact before me, I find it difficult to believe that you, with your education and resources, should have brought your sister to a scene like this."

"I brought him, father," said Louisa, quickly. "I asked him to come."

"I am sorry to hear it. I am very sorry indeed to hear it. It makes Thomas no better, and it makes you worse, Louisa."

She looked at her father again, but no tear fell down her cheek.

"You Thomas and you, to whom the circle of the sciences is open, Thomas and you, who may be said to be replete with facts; Thomas and you, who have been trained to mathematical exactness; Thomas and you here!" cried Mr. Gradgrind. "In this degraded position! I am amazed."

The children return home in disgrace, and are met by their father's friend Mr Bounderby, an equally strict Victorian gentleman.

"Well!" blustered Mr Bounderby, "what's the matter? What is young Thomas in the dumps about?"

He spoke of young Thomas, but he looked at Louisa.

"We were peeping at the circus," muttered Louisa haughtily, without lifting up her eyes, "and father caught us."

"And Mrs Gradgrind," said her husband in a lofty manner, "I should as soon have expected to find my children reading poetry."

"Dear me," whimpered Mrs Gradgrind. "How can you, Louisa and Thomas! I wonder at you. I declare you're enough to make one regret ever having had a family at all. I have a great mind to say I wish I hadn't. Then what would you have done, I should like to know."

Mr Gradgrind did not seem favourably impressed by these cogent remarks. He frowned impatiently.

"As if, with my head in its present throbbing state, you couldn't go and look at the shells and minerals and things provided for you, instead of circuses!" said Mrs Gradgrind.

© **Topical Resources.** May be photocopied for classroom use only.

Teacher's Notes

National Literacy Strategy Year 6 Term 2:

To parody a literacy text describing stock characters and plot structure, language, etc.

Read the passage aloud to the children at least twice. Explain that it is set in Victorian times and that Thomas and Louisa's father was a factory owner, who expected his children to spend all their spare time studying information books. Ask the children to find evidence of this in the passage they have just read. Explain that the circus was not considered by Mr Gradgrind to be suitable for the children. He saw it as a waste of valuable studying time. The other character we meet is Mr. Gradgrind's friend Mr. Bounderby, who shares similar views on how the children should spend their time.

Ask the children how they would describe Mr and Mrs Gradgrind, and their children Louisa and Tom. It would be very useful to find a photograph of a rather stern looking Victorian family, so that the children can build up an image of the Gradgrinds. Ask the children to pick out words and phrases which make them realise that the book was written in Victorian times.

Explain to the class that they are now going to write the story which precedes the passage, where Louisa and Tom disobey their parents and go to see the circus. Their story should begin from the point at which they secretly manage to slip out of the house. It should go on to describe what happens when they go to the circus, what they see and hear and how they feel. The story will end at the point when Mr Gradgrind catches them. The children should write the story in the third person and should try to imitate the formal Dickensian style, as far as possible. It may be useful to gather together on the blackboard some distinctly Victorian words and phrases that could be incorporated in their story e.g. 'in the name of wonder, idleness and folly'.

The children should make a plan using the story writing frame. There is a Writing Support sheet for those children who struggle to find ideas. The children should go on to write the story in full. It would be interesting to read some of the more successful stories aloud, so the children can evaluate how far each writer has achieved writing in the style of the text.

THE CIRCUS

Name: _____ **Date:** _____

Here are some words and ideas to help you. Can you add to these?

Setting

The Gradgrind's House:
dark, gloomy, large, old,
nursery, study, books,
maids, servants, cook.

The Circus:
noisy, music, colourful,
exciting, trapeze,
elephants, jugglers, tight-
rope walk, lion-tamer,
clowns.

Characters

Thomas:
older, taller/shorter,
brother, shy, quiet,
excited, afraid, brave.

Louisa:
sister, brave, clever at
planning, secretive,
talkative, worried, afraid.

Mr Gradgrind:
strict, gloomy, serious, angry,
dull, boring, never laughs.

 © **Topical Resources.** May be photocopied for classroom use only.

Writing Frame

45

Name: _____ **Date:** _____

The story setting:

Characters in the story:

How do the children manage to secretly leave the house? How does the story begin?

What happens at the circus? Who do they meet? What do they see?

How are they caught by Mr Gradgrind? How is the story resolved?

© **Topical Resources.** May be photocopied for classroom use only.

Silver

Slowly, silently, now the Moon

Walks the night in her silver shoon;

This way, and that, she peers, and sees

Silver fruit upon silver trees;

One by one the casements catch

Her beams beneath the silvery thatch;

Couched in his kennel, like a log,

With paws of silver sleeps the dog;

From their shadowy cote the white breasts peep

Of doves in a silver-feathered sleep;

A harvest mouse goes scampering by,

With silver claws and silver eye;

And moveless fish in the water gleam

By silver reeds in a silver stream.

by Walter de la Mare

These 2 lines rhyme. Bracket together the other lines that rhyme.

Highlight the words which make the moon seem like a person.

Underline the simile which describes how the dog sleeps.

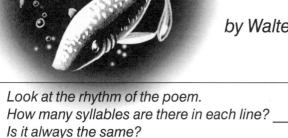

Look at the rhythm of the poem.
How many syllables are there in each line? ___
Is it always the same? _____

Highlight in a different colour, parts of the poem you particularly like.

Put a ring around the word 'silver'.
It is used ____ times in the poem to emphasise...
_____
_____

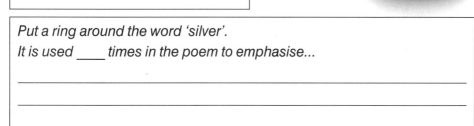

© **Topical Resources.** May be photocopied for classroom use only

An Annotation of the poem "Silver" by Walter de la Mare

National Literacy Strategy Year 6 Term 3:

To annotate passages in detail in response to specific questions.

Read the poem 'Silver' aloud to the children and then get the children to read the poem aloud. Only by actually doing this themselves will the children begin to experience the real effect of the poetry. Ask the children for an initial reaction to the poem. What do they like about the poem? Why? What do they think the poem is about?

It would then be useful to go through the poem, line by line, to ensure the children have understood each little cameo or any unfamiliar words like 'casements'.

Talk about what De La Mare is describing? Go on to talk about why he repeats the word silver so frequently in the poem. Does it add to the effect? If so how? Examine the idea of the moon being personified as a lady and the effectiveness of this. Introduce or revise the term personification (when an inanimate object is given human characteristics). Find the simile which compares the dog to a log. Is this effective? Examine the rhyme scheme of the poem. Does it aid the effectiveness of the poem?

Again look at the rhythm of the poem. Say the poem aloud line by line to work out the syllables in each line. Again, is the regular rhythm effective? Does it add to the poem in any way? Ask the children to mark any part of the poem that they particularly like/dislike and to try and say why they feel that way.

Following on from the class discussion ask the children to annotate the poem answering the questions on the photocopiable sheet.

Personal Response

National Literacy Strategy Year 6 Term 3:

To use a reading journal effectively to raise and refine personal responses to a text and prepare for discussion.
To write summaries of books or parts of books, deciding on priorities relevant to purpose.

The children should be given a copy of the photocopiable Personal Response sheet to complete after they have finished reading a particular novel. They should firstly endeavour to briefly summarise the plot. Then they should think about the characters in the novel and decide which is their favourite and why. Finally, they should consider the part of the story they most enjoyed and the audience to whom they would recommend the book, thinking carefully about age and reading interest.

This 'personal response' sheet is a simple writing frame which is a good introduction to writing a formal book review. It leads the children through the aspects they need to consider prior to writing. The 'Personal Response' sheets could be a useful activity to carry out before a classroom discussion on books the children have enjoyed or disliked. It ensures that the children formulate carefully considered opinions and do not just make the statement "because I liked it/didn't like it".

The 'personal response' sheets could be put together in a class folder/file readily available to all children, so they can make informed choices before selecting their next book. This needs to be displayed in an accessible place in the classroom and opportunity needs to be given for the children to refer to the folder prior to library or book time.

Personal Response

Name: _____ **Date:** _____

A personal response to the book.. . . . .

by . . . .

A summary of the plot (what happens in the story)

_____

_____

_____

_____

The characters in the story

_____

_____

_____

_____

In your own words, relate the parts of the story you found most exciting or funny or sad. Try to say why you chose each part.

_____

_____

_____

_____

Who would you recommend this book to? Think about age range and whether it might be enjoyed by a girl or boy. Think about whether it would it be suitable for children who enjoy a particular genre e.g. science fiction or historical stories.

_____

_____

_____

© **Topical Resources.** May be photocopied for classroom use only.

Back Cover Blurb

Space Monsters
by Fiona Smith

Set in the year 2075, 'Space Monsters' tells of three children's amazing adventures in outer space. Their spacecraft crash lands on Planet Od. How will the gallant young astronauts save themselves from a mob of vicious space monsters?

'Compulsive reading, Fiona Smith's latest novel is Science Fiction at its best'
The Times
'Wonderful - I just couldn't put it down'
The Guardian

WINNER OF THE CHILDREN'S BOOK AWARD

U.K £3.50
AUST $7.99
CAN $5.95
A Wise Owl Book
ISBN 1-872977-48-1

7 31452 59522 5

Spooky Verse

Chosen by Sam Smith

In this treasure chest of verse, there are poems old and new. Some are funny, some are scary, but they're all a joy to read. You'll want to keep this book forever!

'Spooky Verse is a terrific selection for 9 - 13 year olds'
The Times

Cover illustrations by Sonia Browning

SEAL BOOKS
POETRY/NON FICTION
U.K. £3.50
N.Z. $11.95
ISBN 1-872977-56-0

8 09274 02042 0

© **Topical Resources.** May be photocopied for classroom use only.

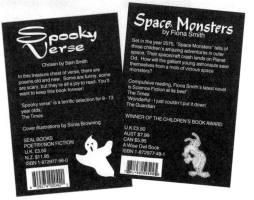

Back Cover Blurb

National Literacy Strategy Year 6 Term 3:

To write a brief synopsis of a text, e.g. for back cover blurb.

Read the back cover blurb pages together with the children. Talk about how the pictures and language contribute to its effectiveness. Do these make you want to read on? Talk about the effect of the newspaper quotes. Note the other information on the blurb page - publisher name and logo, price in U.K. and abroad, ISBN number and bar code. Discuss the importance of variety of fonts.

Then, give the children a selection of book titles and ask them to design the blurb page for one of them.
Titles might include:
Dangerous Journey by Mustapha Explore
Funny Poems by A.V.A. Laugh
Lost in Space by Mill, Key and Way
The Tale of the Lost Kingdom by B.Y. Gone

These will need to be planned carefully using the writing frame and could be an excellent desk top publishing activity.

Back Cover Blurb

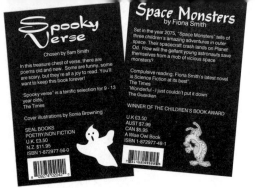

Name: _____ **Date:** _____

Book Title.. . . . .

by . . . .

An exciting summary of the plot / or a quote from the book.

_____
_____
_____
_____
_____
_____
_____
_____
_____
_____

Special award: _____
_____

Newspaper review quote: _____
_____
_____

Price UK £_____
        NZ $_____

ISBN:

Bar Code No:

© **Topical Resources.** May be photocopied for classroom use only

People to Like and Dislike

Miss Trunchbull, the Headmistress, was something else altogether. She was a gigantic holy terror, a fierce tyrannical monster who frightened the life out of the pupils and teachers alike.

There was an aura of menace about her even at a distance, and when she came up close you could almost feel the dangerous heat radiating from her as from a red-hot rod of metal. When she marched - Miss Trunchbull never walked, she always marched like a storm-trooper with long strides and arms a swinging - when she marched along a corridor you could actually hear her snorting as she went, and if a group of children happened to be in her path, she ploughed right on through them like a tank, with small people bouncing off her to left and right.

Thank goodness we don't meet many people like her in this world, although they do exist and all of us are likely to come across at least one of them in a lifetime. If you ever do, you should behave as you would if you met an enraged rhinoceros out in the bush - climb up the nearest tree and stay there until it has gone away.
From Matilda by Road Dahl.

I was staying at the time with my uncle and his wife. Although she was my aunt, I never thought of her as anything but the wife of my uncle, partly because he was so big and trumpeting and red-hairy and used to fill every inch of the hot little house like an old buffalo squeezed into an airing cupboard, and partly because she was so small and silk and quick and made no noise at all as she whisked about on padded paws, dusting the china dogs, feeding the buffalo, setting the mousetraps that never caught her; and once she sneaked out of the room, to squeak in a nook or nibble in the hayloft, you forgot she had ever been there.

But there he was, always a steaming hulk of an uncle, his braces straining like hawsers, crammed behind the counter of the tiny shop at the front of the house, and breathing like a brass band; or guzzling and blustery in the kitchen over his gutsy supper, too big for everything except the great black boats of his boots. As he ate, the house grew smaller; he billowed out over the furniture, the loud check meadow of his waistcoat littered, as though after a picnic, with cigarette ends, peelings, cabbage-stalks, birds' bones, gravy; and the forest fire of his hair crackled among the hooked hams from the ceiling. She was so small she could hit him only if she stood on a chair, and every Saturday night at half past ten he would lift her up, under his arm, on to a chair in the kitchen so that she could hit him on the head with whatever was handy, which was always a china dog.
From A Prospect of the Sea by Dylan Thomas.

© **Topical Resources.** May be photocopied for classroom use only.

People to Like and Dislike

National Literacy Strategy Year 6 Term 3:

To compare texts in writing, drawing out their different styles and pre-occupations, strengths and weaknesses, their different values and appeals to a reader.

Read each passage in turn, at least twice. Talk about what sort of character Dahl portrays Miss Trunchbull to be. What aspects of Miss Trunchbull does Dahl concentrate on? Which parts of the description do you like best? Choose any words or phrases you think are particularly effective. Are there any aspects of the passage which you did not like?

Then, look at the Dylan Thomas descriptions of his Aunt and Uncle. Talk about how you would imagine them to look and act. Did you enjoy the passage? Are there any particular words or phrases that you feel are especially effective? Dylan Thomas uses very unusual and unlikely comparisons. Pick out some of these from the passage. Do you like the way he puts words together in this way or does it not appeal to you and why? Ask the children to decide which of the two descriptions they enjoyed the most, giving reasons. The children should use the writing frame to write a comparison of the texts.

The children could then write a character description of someone they know well in the style of either Dahl or Thomas. These will take several drafts to achieve success. The effectiveness of their attempts to write in the style of the writers, can be assessed by reading their descriptions aloud. This has to be done in a sympathetic and sensitive way, concentrating on positive criticism.

People to Like and Dislike

Name: _____ **Date:** _____

Which passage did you enjoy the most and why? How do you imagine the characters that are being described? Describe how you imagine them.

_____
_____
_____
_____

Pick out three or four phrases that you found particularly descriptive? Try and say why you liked each.

_____
_____
_____
_____

Were there any phrases, or parts of the descriptions, which you particularly disliked? Choose two and say why you disliked them.

_____
_____
_____
_____
_____
_____
_____

Now choose someone you know very well. Write a character sketch of them in about 15 lines in either the style of Dahl or Thomas. Use the sub heading 'A character description of _____ in the style of _____.' *Write on the back of this sheet.*

© **Topical Resources.** May be photocopied for classroom use only.

A Book Review

National Literacy Strategy Year 6 Term 3:

To write a brief helpful review tailored for real audiences.

It is helpful if a class discussion on favourite books can precede the written work. Children can share their ideas with others and recommend titles and authors to their peers. Try to encourage the children to summarise the plot in their own words and to consider favourite characters and episodes they particularly enjoyed. They should be encouraged to consider the age range of the child for which the book might be suitable. It would be useful to ensure the children understand the term genre and consider this in their discussion.

The children should then go on to write their book review. There is a writing frame to aid the children with their planning. The reviews can then be drafted. The finished reviews could be combined together to make a Class Review Book. This could be left in a prominent place in the classroom, or could be passed around for individuals to read, prior to choosing a new book.

A Book Review

Name: _____ **Date:** _____

A Book Review of.. . . . .

by . . . .

Illustrated by . . . .

Summarise the story in this paragraph. Avoid making it any longer than 6 sentences. You could also mention if the book is illustrated and if you feel this helps the story.

_____

_____

_____

_____

Choose one or two favourite characters - describe them and say why they appeal to you and why you identify with them.

_____

_____

_____

_____

In your own words, relate the parts of the story you found most exciting or funny or sad. Try to say why you chose each part.

_____

_____

_____

_____

To whom would you recommend this book? Think about age range and whether it might be enjoyed by a girl or boy. Think about whether it would it be suitable for children who enjoy a particular genre. e.g. science fiction or historical stories.

_____

_____

_____

_____

© **Topical Resources.** May be photocopied for classroom use only.

In the ceiling was a small trapdoor that led into the attic. A ladder lay between his bed and the wall. Quietly he removed it, hooked it under the trap and climbed up.

Hidden between the water tank and the felt jacket around it was his rifle. He was a member of the Boys' Rifle Brigade and had used it in the siege of Warsaw. It was loaded. He took it out and quickly climbed down to his room. The noise in the room below had stopped. Looking out of the window into the street, he saw a Nazi van waiting outside the front door. Two storm troopers were taking his mother down the steps, and she was struggling.

Quietly Edek lifted the window sash till it was half open. He dared not shoot in case he hit his mother.

From " The Silver Sword" by Ian Serraillier

Escape!

He had to wait till she was in the van and the doors were being closed. His first shot hit a soldier in the arm. Yelling, he jumped in beside the driver. With the next two shots Edek aimed at the tyres. One punctured the rear wheel, but the van got away, skidding and roaring up the street. His other shots went wide. With the butt of his rifle he broke down the door and ran down to his sisters. They were locked in too. He burst open the door.

Bronia was sitting up in bed and Ruth was trying to calm her. She was almost as distraught herself. Only the effort to comfort Bronia kept her from losing control.
'I hit one of the swine,' said Edek.
'That was very silly of you,' said Ruth. 'They'll come back for us now.'
'I couldn't let them take Mother away like that,' said Edek. 'Oh, be quiet, Bronia! Howling won't help.'
'We must get away from here before they come back,' said Ruth
With some difficulty she dressed Bronia, while Edek went into the hall to fetch overcoats and boots and fur caps.

There was no time for Ruth to dress properly. She put on a coat over her nightdress and wound a woollen scarf round Bronia.
'We can't get out the front way,' said Edek. 'There's another van coming. I heard the whistle.'
'What about the back?' said Ruth
'The wall's too high. We'd never get Bronia over. Besides, there are Nazis billeted in that street. There's only one way - over the roof.'

58
© **Topical Resources.** May be photocopied for classroom use only.

Escape!

National Literacy Strategy Year 6 Term 3:

To write an extended story, worked on over time on a theme identified in reading.

Before reading the photocopiable passage, explain to the children that the story is set in the second world war in Poland. Nazi soldiers had taken away Joseph Balicki, the children's father. The children are asleep in bed, when the Nazi soldiers return for their mother. Edek is terrified that he and his sisters will be the next victims. Then read the passage aloud.

After reading, talk to the children about the background to the passage. The children may well have some knowledge of the history of the period from books, film, T.V. programmes, history lessons, etc. Talk about how it must have felt to have been Edek and his sisters. Discuss the nightmare of concentration camps and the idea of families being split, just as the Balicki family have been in the passage.

The children could then go on to write the chapter that follows on from this passage entitled, 'The Escape'. The chapter could begin with how the children escape over the roof, and where they finally find refuge. There is a writing frame for this chapter and also a writing support sheet for those children who struggle to think of ideas. If time allows, the children could go on to write further chapters on how the children survive and if or how they are finally re-united with their parents.

The children may decide to work as a group and delegate a chapter to each member. Thus, the children could end up with a 'mini novel' developed on the theme. It would be interesting to read the remainder of 'The Silver Sword', and to compare how Serraillier has developed the theme of escape and divided families.

Escape!

Name: _____ **Date:** _____

Here are some words and ideas to help you. Can you add to these?

Setting
Roof-Top:
Nazi soldiers waiting,
guns shooting, trucks,
jeeps, tanks, roof high
above the street,
chimneys, slates,
darkness, moonlight.

Shelter:
barn / empty house,
candle light, mice, rats,
old furniture, cold.

Characters
Edek:
older brother, age?
strong, tall, brave, clever,
fit, cheerful, helpful,
can fire a gun, protects.

Ruth:
sister, has to be mother
to Bronia, caring, afraid,
comforts Bronia.

Bronia:
young child, afraid, tired,
crying, sad, upset.

 © **Topical Resources.** May be photocopied for classroom use onl'

Escape!

Name: _____ Date: _____

The story setting:

Characters in the story:

The story begins with the children's escape over the roof? Describe what happens:

Where do the children go next? What problems do they face?

Where do they end up? Who do they meet?

How does the story end? Are they safe? Do the Nazis discover them?

© Topical Resources. May be photocopied for classroom use only.

The Seasons

Winter withering
Coating brown dead shrivelled
leaves
In glistening frost.

Blackbirds' sweet singing
Joins with yellow daffodil,
Welcome Spring is here!

Warmth of trembling breeze,
Gently ruffling the perfect rose
Whose scent fills warm nights.

Golden crisp leaves fall
As the glowing sun rises
On the newly mown hay.

© **Topical Resources.** May be photocopied for classroom use onl

National Literacy Strategy Year 6 Term 3:

To write a sequence of poems linked by theme or form, e.g. a Haiku Calendar.

Read the poems aloud and talk about their effectiveness at painting a mental image with words. Which are the most effective and why do the children think this?

Explain to the children that making a picture with words is not as easy as it looks at first. Japanese Haiku poetry attempts to be brief but very precise. The poems have three lines, of five, seven and five syllables and often end in a noun. In the poem, the poet takes just two or three simple images and writes them in as few words as possible in the pattern of three lines. The poems are often about nature or the seasons.

The children could try to write their own haiku calendar, based on the seasons, or the life cycle of a frog, butterfly or fruit tree. There is a writing support page to help those children who struggle to think of ideas.

These would need to be drafted several times. The children could put their poems into a class anthology of Haiku, which could in turn, be passed on to other children in different classes to read.

The Seasons

Name: _____   **Date:** _____

Here are some ideas to start you writing. Can you write some Haiku of your own?

A Butterfly

In the chrysalis.
Slowly growing and changing.
Butterfly is born!

Life Cycle of a Frog

Frog spawn in a still and silent pond.
Small black tadpoles darting around.
Back legs first, then front legs growing.
Tails shrink.
Tiny frog leaves the pond.
To live in long grass and under stones.

Seasons

Winter
dark short cold and frosty days.
Spring
buds, new life, blossom on trees,
growth, warmth, lambs in fields.
Summer
long warm days, playing out, gardens
filled with flowers, holidays, seaside,
country.
Autumn
leaves fall from trees, brown, yellow,
red, ripe fruit, shorter days, return to
school.

Fruit Tree

Winter
bare brown branches, hard and dead.
Spring
green buds spring into leaf, blossom
pink and white.
Summer
leaves grow large and green, fruit
grows, swelling with sun and rain.
Autumn
fruit is full grown, apple / pear / plum,
juicy plump, ripe and ready to pick.

 © Topical Resources. May be photocopied for classroom use onl